LIVERPOOL ROYAL INFIRMARY

NURSES' LEAGUE

COMMEMORATING THE 75th ANNIVERSARY OF THE NURSES' LEAGUE

Foreword by Mrs Ann Spencer,
Nurses' League President

Dedicated to the Memory of
Emeritus Professor Kate Russell 1944 - 2007

President of the Liverpool Royal Infirmary
Nurses' Training School Nurses' League 2003 - 2007

Front Cover - Liverpool Royal Infirmary 1908
Back Cover - L.R.I. Staff Nurses 1963

First Published 2008 by Countyvise Limited, 14 Appin Road, Birkenhead, Wirral CH41 9HH.

Copyright © 2008 Liverpool Royal Infirmary Nurses' Training School Nurses' League

British Library Cataloguing in Publication Data.
A catalogue record for this book is available from the British Library.

ISBN 978 1 901231 99 1

CONTENTS

ACKNOWLEDGEMENTS

The Nurses' League would like to thank everyone who has loaned or donated photographs for this book. Special thanks go to Liverpool Record Office, Liverpool Daily Post and Foresight Centre for their photographs and assistance.

Jen Berry

Margaret Blair

Hazel Brown

Dorothea Davies

Anne Farquhar

Moira Featherstone

Edwina Fysh

Jean Hall

Ruth Halsall

Betty Hoare

Mary Howe

Barbara Leech

Sylvia Lewis

Liverpool Daily Post

Liverpool Record Office

Gwen Moreland

Jocelyn Moore

Estate of Elizabeth and Gwenda Morgan

Glenys Nicks

Sylvia Norcott

Gwenda Pratt

Pat Shillington

Ann Spencer

Lynn Westbury and staff, Foresight Centre

Elizabeth Wilkinson

Jean Woods

Elspeth Yule

FOREWORD

This year, 2008, the Nurses' League celebrates its 75th Anniversary.

In recognition of this achievement, this book of photographs has been compiled, which we hope will evoke many happy memories of your time at the 'Royal'. We all have particular memories of people and occasions that are special to us and we have endeavoured to select photographs which offer the broadest possible view of the many decades of nursing at our historic hospital.

Compiling this book has been a team effort, but I would like to record special thanks to Pat Shillington, who was ably assisted by Mary Howe, Pat Lambert and Moira Featherstone, all Committee members. Pat and Mary spent many hours at the Liverpool Record Office, researching old photographs associated with the Royal Infirmary.

This book is dedicated to the memory of Kate Russell, President of the Nurses' League, 2003 - 2007, who sadly died while still in office. The idea to produce a pictorial record to commemorate this anniversary, was initiated while Kate was President.

We hope you enjoy these photographs, which give a fascinating glimpse of times gone by.

Ann Spencer
President

INTRODUCTION

In 2008 the Executive Committee of the Liverpool Royal Infirmary Nurses' League produced this book to commemorate the 75th Anniversary of the League. The book is for everyone who has been associated with Liverpool Royal Infirmary and the City of Liverpool.

The Royal Infirmary's close ties with the city of Liverpool could not be overlooked in the production of this book as the city celebrated it's 800th Birthday in 2007 and European Capital of Culture in 2008.

The Liverpool Royal Infirmary Nurses' League was formed in 1933 by Miss Mary Jones, Matron, with the aim of forming a bond between nurses who trained at the Liverpool Royal Infirmary.

The Royal Infirmary, Pembroke Place, was opened in 1890, the third building in Liverpool to use the title. In 1978 hospital services where transferred into the newly built Royal Liverpool Hospital in Prescot Street. In 1994, after being empty for 15 years, the Grade 2 listed building was bought by Liverpool University for £1, their aim being to develop the site and restore the buildings to their former glory for use as an interface between the University and regional industry and commerce. So far a number of wards have been converted into department lecture areas, the ground floor is a doctors' surgery and the Chapel a conference centre.

Links with the Royal Infirmary continue as the Liverpool Royal Infirmary Nurses' League hold their Annual General Meeting and Reunion in the former Chapel, located in the Foresight Centre.

An appeal was made in the local press asking readers for photographs for the book. The response was very encouraging. We were especially delighted to have been lent photographs of the war years. Similarly, league members were cajoled into searching their lofts to find forgotten photographs. The chosen photographs present a history of the Royal Infirmary until it closed in 1978.

The Committee have tried to include as many group photographs as possible, however, despite the sterling efforts of League members to put names to faces, it has not been possible to name everyone. Equally, many hours were spent verifying dates.

Photographs have been categorised to depict various elements of hospital life over the years. We were particularly inundated with photographs of Christmas activities!

We hope these photographs of the Royal Infirmary will bring back happy memories of your Alma Mater.

MISS MARY JONES O.B.E. A.R.R.C. M.A. S.R.N.
1880 - 1975
President of the Nurses' League 1933 - 1975

Miss Mary Jones commenced nurse training at the Liverpool Royal Infirmary in 1908, aged 28, having previously worked as a governess.

She qualified in 1911 and was appointed a Ward Sister. Over the next 9 years she was Housekeeping Sister, Home Sister and Sister Tutor before becoming Assistant Matron in 1917. She was appointed Matron of the Infirmary on 1 January 1925, a position she held for 22 years until her retirement in February 1947, having spent almost 40 years at the Liverpool Royal Infirmary.

Miss Jones founded The Liverpool Royal Infirmary Nurses' Training School League, for past and present nurses, who had completed their course of training at the Royal Infirmary. At the inaugural meeting, held on 21 October 1933, she was elected President.

Miss Mary Jones in 1908

She was President of the Liverpool Branch of the Royal College of Nursing and President of the RCN from 1940 - 1942, the first provincial Matron to become President of the College. In 1945 she was elected Vice-President of the General Nursing Council. In 1952, an oak screen was erected in the East corner of Liverpool Cathedral, as an acknowledgment and appreciation of Miss Jones' contribution to the Liverpool branch of the RCN, over 27 years.

Miss Jones served in the Territorial Army Nursing Service, being appointed Principal Matron of the 8th (1Western) General Hospital in 1930, a position she held until the dissolution of the service in 1950. She was presented to Queen Mary when she visited the hospital to inspect members of the Territorial Nursing Service. On the outbreak of the Second World War, Miss Jones was appointed Sector Matron by the Ministry of Health.

Miss Jones received a number of honours in recognition of her services to nursing. In 1935 she was awarded the King's Silver Jubilee Medal and attended a Royal Garden Party. In 1937 she was made O.B.E. In 1942, she received an Honorary M.A. from Liverpool University and in 1947 she received the Freedom of the City of Liverpool, commemorated by the presentation of a Silver Salver.

In 1962, a Service of Thanksgiving was held in Liverpool Cathedral and also a Reception at the Town Hall, to commemorate the Centenary year of the Training School. It is recorded that Miss Jones felt so proud as she walked into the Cathedral, to see so many 'Royal' nurses and their families at the Service.

After her retirement, Miss Jones continued to be involved with nursing organisations and regularly visited the Nurses' Training School, having been the Lady Superintendent of the Nurse Training School.

Miss Jones was President of the Nurses' League until her death in 1975.

The Matron, Miss Emmeline Staines and Staff
circa 1882-1889

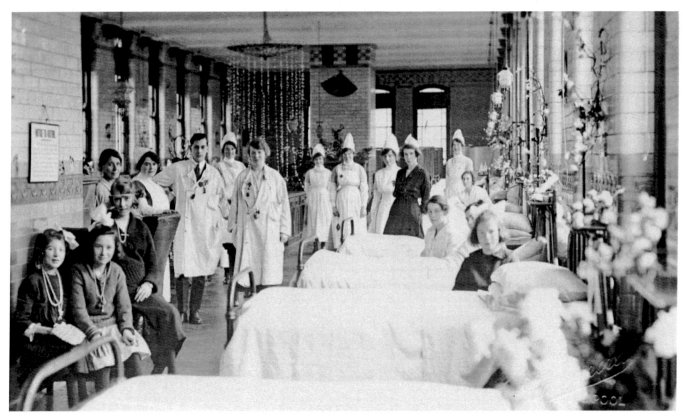

Christmas visiting time on Clarence Ward 1921

Early Days . . . Pre 1933

Dignitaries visit the ward with Miss Mary Jones 31st March 1926

Opening of "New" Nurses Home by The Countess of Derby 1931

A Round Ward 1943

Hospital Front Entrance showing Porters' Lodge and Almoner's Office 1943

Bricks and Mortar

Main Corridor 1943

Staircase to the Doctors' Quarters

This building was opened by The Duke of Clarence and Avondale K.C., 29th October 1890. The foundation stone was laid by The Earl of Derby 29th October 1887.

Bricks and Mortar

Ward 4 during World War II

Lecture Theatre above old Operating Theatre

The Nurses' Home in Ashton Street "Sing-Sing"
Built in 1862 and opened 1st May 1863.

A Nurse's Bedroom in the Nurses' Home - Cedar House.

Bricks and Mortar

The Chapel

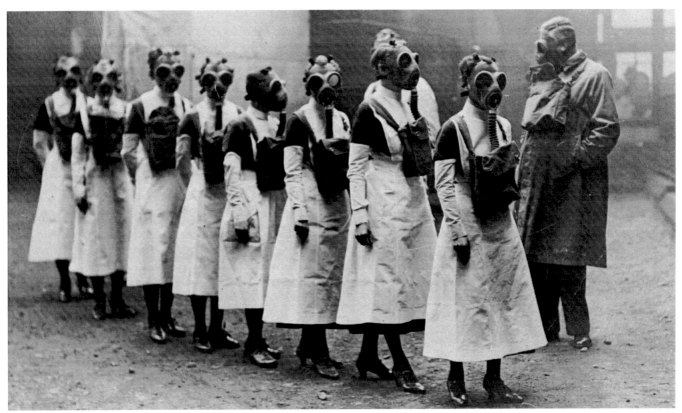

Gas Mask Drill 1939

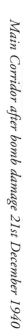

Main Corridor after bomb damage 21st December 1940

Ward 8 after the Blitz 4th May 1941

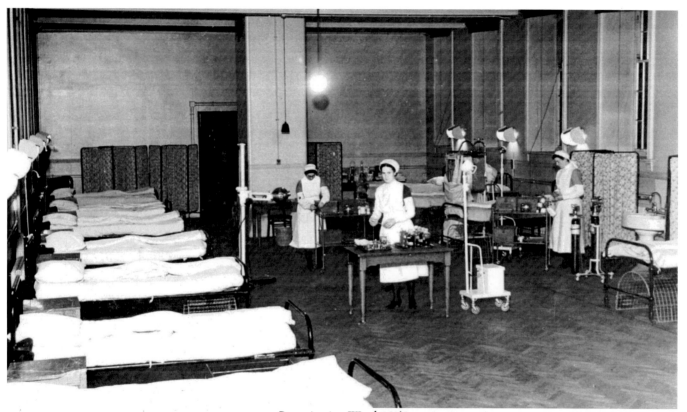

Resuscitation Ward 1940
This ward was kept for the casualties of war. It later became an orthopedic ward

Disinfection Lecture circa 1940
Sister R. Darroch is on the left of the display and Sister Laura Jones far right. Nurse Gibson, later Sister on Ward 9, is on the left of this picture

The War Years

In Mufti 1944
Dorothy Houlton, Betty Eaglesfield,
Rosemary Porterfield, Morfudd Owen

Sisters on V. E. Day

NURSES' HOME

Tea with the Mayor and Mayoress 1933

Nurses' Home

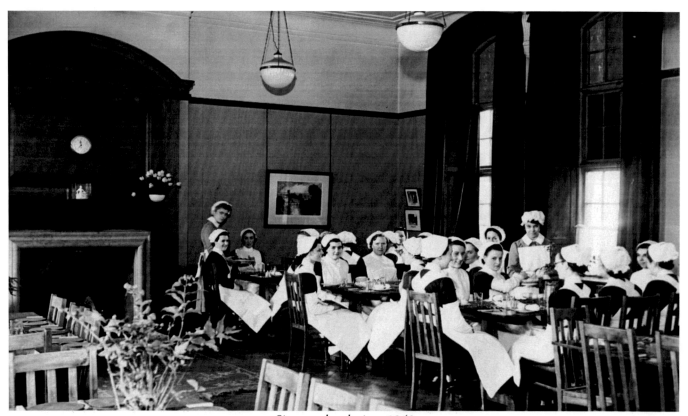

Sisters at lunch circa 1940
Sister Liggins, Home Sister, Sister Entwistle and Sister Horsburgh are in this picture

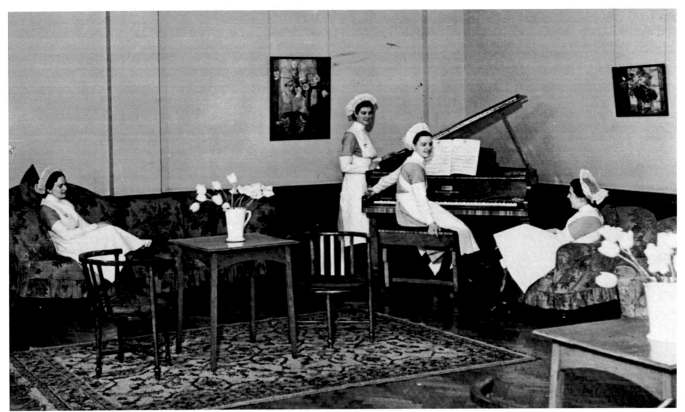

The Rankin Sitting Room

Nurses' Home

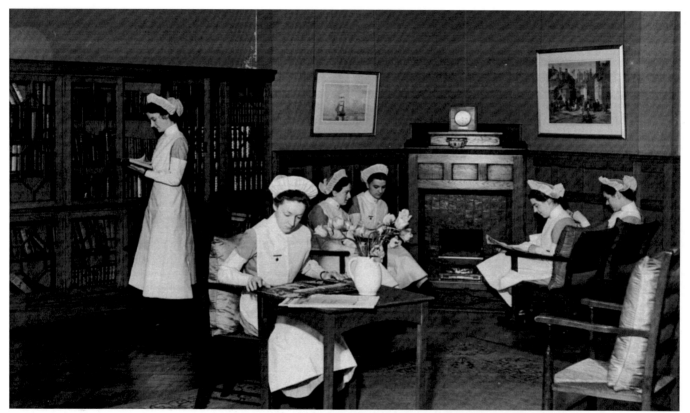

The Walter Harding Library

NURSES AT LEISURE

Late for Duty!

Nurses at Leisure

Fundraising at Red Rose Ball, The Adelphi Hotel, Liverpool 1934

Keeping occupied during the Blitz 1940

Nurses at Leisure

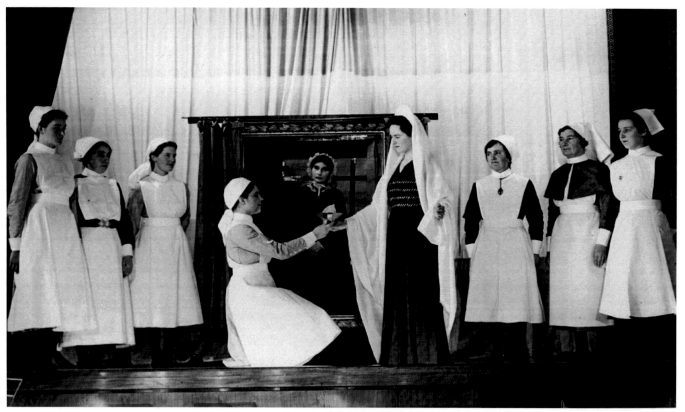

Nurses' Tabloid 1942

Production of Pride and Prejudice by Nursing Staff circa 1944

Walter Harding Tennis Tournament circa 1954, The Royal v Walton Hospital, Liverpool
The winning Royal team are on the left. Margaret Hutton, Betty Whitley Jones, B. Hanson (holding trophy), Elizabeth Wilkinson

Fun and Games on the roof of the Nurses' Home!
August 1961 PTS

Nurses at Leisure

Nurses' Ball, Adelphi Hotel, Liverpool 1966
Jean Ellis, Hilary Davies, Annette Hudson, Janet Griffiths, Anne Lavery, Berni Perton, Barbara Hill and their guests

Traditional procession through the ward. Christmas Eve circa 1930
Florence Jones, Sister (Ward 5) leads the Carol Singers

Christmas

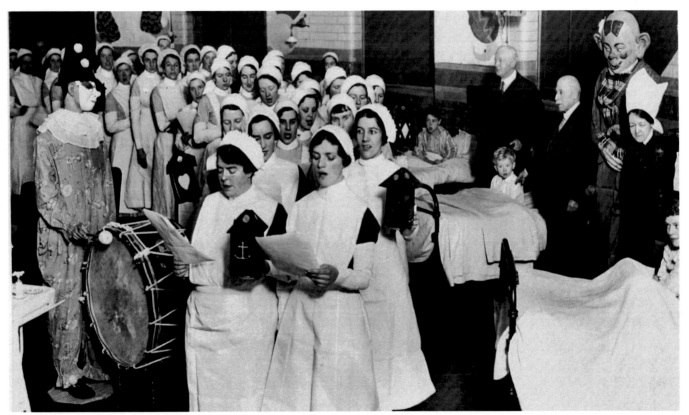

Christmas Eve 1933

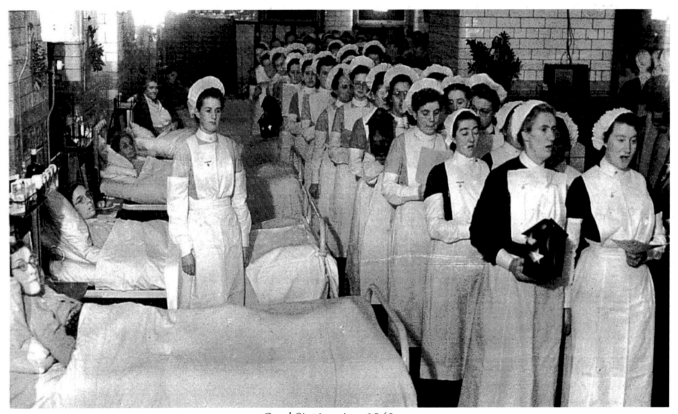

Carol Singing circa 1940
Sister Egerton, Sister Tolman, Sister Gale lead the procession, as Staff Nurse Pickering watches from the bedside

Christmas

Traditional procession through the hospital lead by Sister Taylor, Sister Price, Sister Haynes and Sister Egerton circa 1950

Christmas Carols in the Chapel 1954

Christmas

Sister Garsden and Sister Greenough celebrate Christmas with their staff 1959

Christmas Dinner on Ward 8

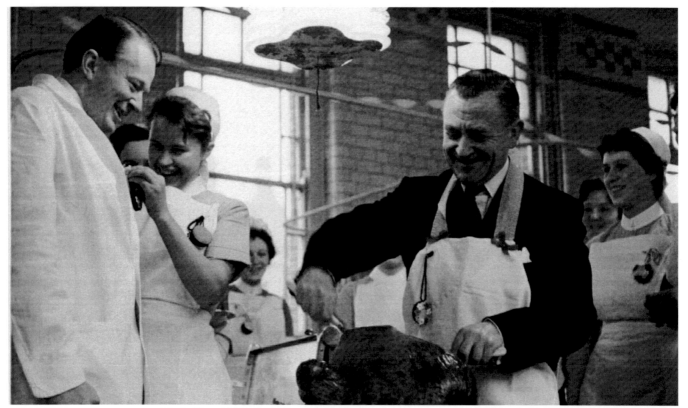

Mr J. Howell Hughes Consultant Surgeon, carves the turkey on Ward 8

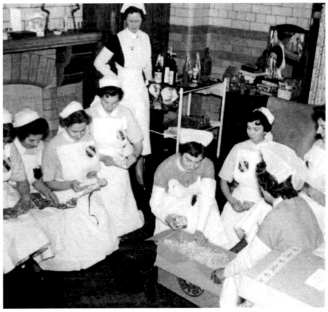

Christmas on Ward 7 with Sister E. Yule

Christmas

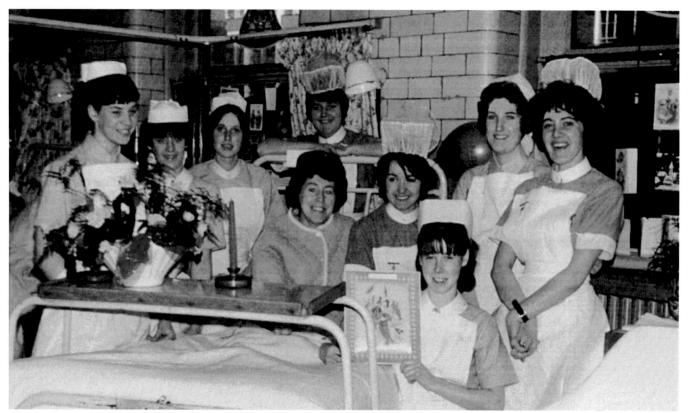

Christmas on Ward 1 1965

ON THE WARDS

Ward 5 1950

On The Wards

Sister's Desk Ward 5 1950
Sister Betty Eaglesfield

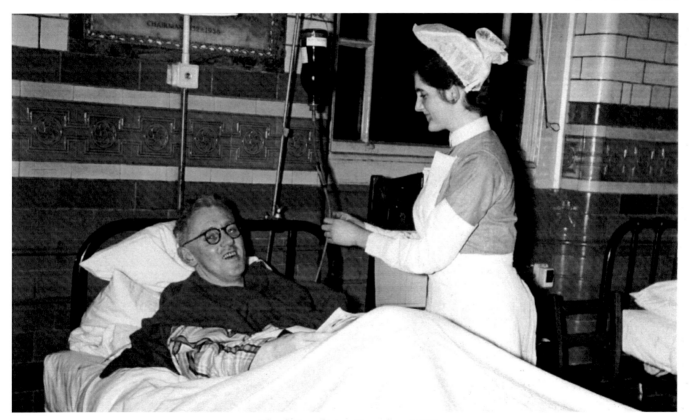

Blood Transfusion Procedure 1953

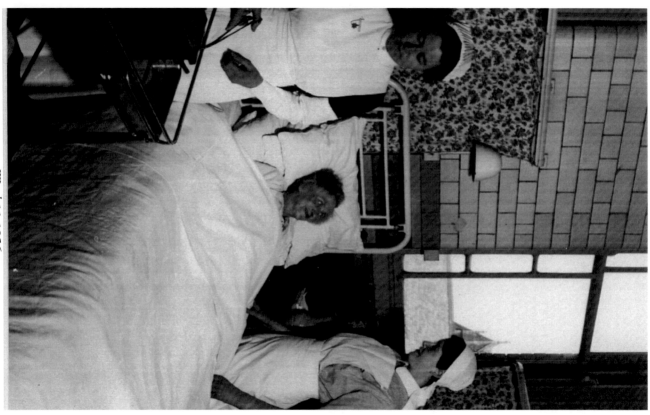

Ward 11 1956
Sister Margaret Ashby and Nurse Edwina Fysh

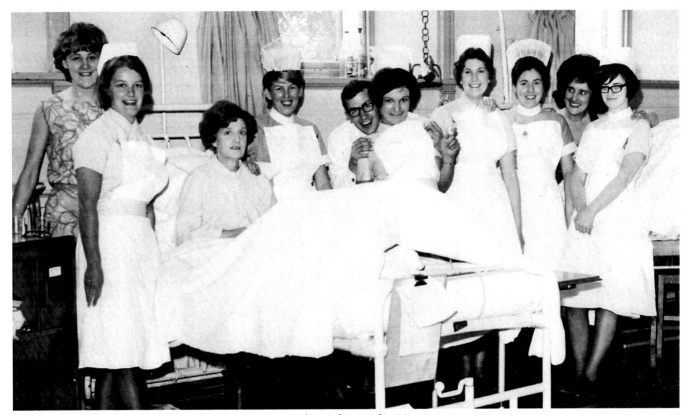

Orthopaedic Ward 1965

On The Wards

"It helps me cough, nurse!"

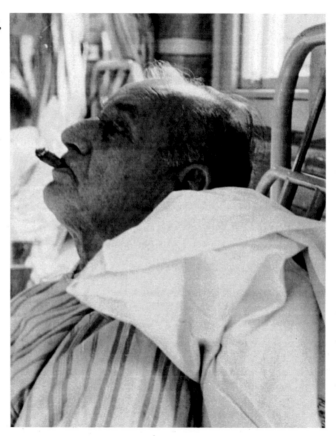

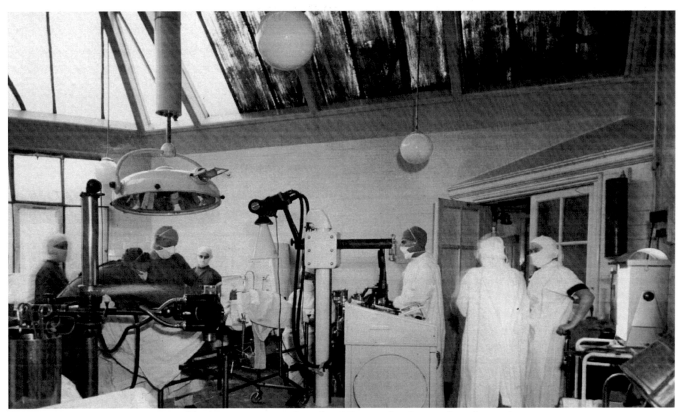

Old Theatres - Natural Light - Waiting for the window cleaners!

Operating Theatres

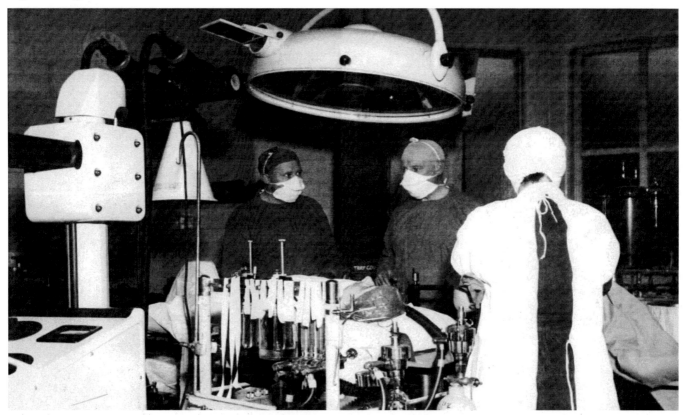

Anaesthetics have improved over the years!

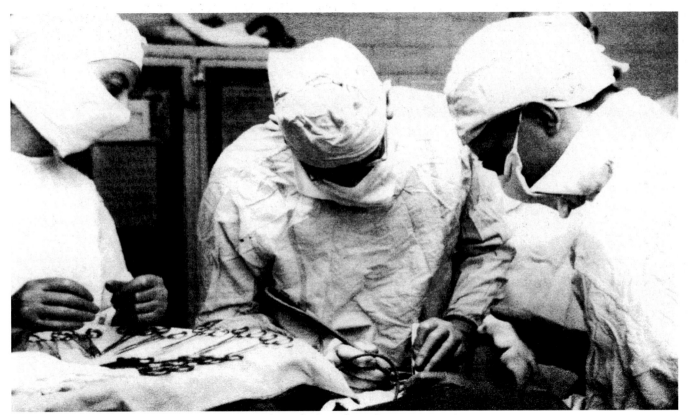

Mr Hugh Reid, Consultant Surgeon, operating
Assisted by Miss Helen Brett, Theatre Superintendant

PRESIDENTS OF LIVERPOOL ROYAL INFIRMARY NURSES' LEAGUE

Miss Mary Jones,
1933 - 1975

Miss Lilian Poueits,
1976 - 1986

Miss Rebecca Haynes,
1986 - 1994

Miss Joan Tolman,
1994 - 1997

PRESIDENTS OF LIVERPOOL ROYAL INFIRMARY NURSES' LEAGUE

Miss Ruth Halsall
1997 - 2001

Miss Jean Woods
2001 - 2003

Mrs Kate Russell
2003 - 2007

Mrs Ann Spencer
2007 -

"ENTER YE TO LEARN. GO FORTH TO SERVE"

Nurse Training School in the Royal Infirmary circa 1940
Sister Laura Jones, Tutor

The Preliminary Training School, Woolton, Liverpool
Opened as United Liverpool Hospitals' Training School 1954

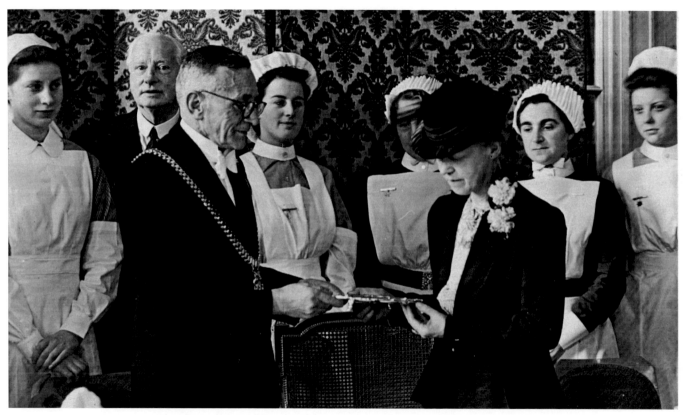

Freedom of City of Liverpool being presented to Miss Mary Jones 1947

Prize Winners 1946

Presentations

Prize Winners April 1947
From left Matron L. Poueits, Betty Berry, Dorothy Ellis, Jocelyn Hollingworth, Sir John Shute, Mayor and Mayoress, Elspeth Yule.

Prize Winners circa 1950
with Matron T. Turner

Presentations

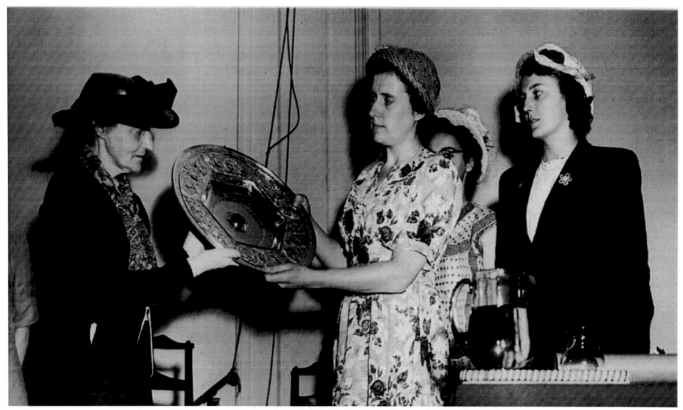

Marion Agnes Gullen Trophy 1949
Ruth Halsall, Joyce Roden and Eirlys Vaughan receiving the trophy at the Royal College of Nursing, London from Marion Agnes Gullen

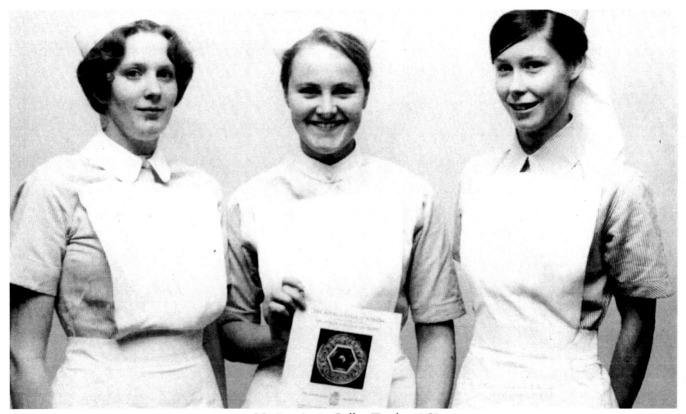

Marion Agnes Gullen Trophy 1965
Sheila Roberts, Elizabeth Buckley and Jen Chambers receiving second prize at Great Ormond Street Childrens' Hospital, London

Presentations

Princess Alexandra of Kent arriving at the Royal for Centenary Prizegiving
17th April 1962

Centenary of Royal Infirmary Nurses' Training School 1962
Princess Alexandra presenting awards at the prizegiving

Presentations

Prize Winners 1963
Miss R. Haynes, Matron S. Jackson, Lady Rathborne, Claire Wood, Liz Stevens, Val Daniels, Mr W. L. Bateson

Prize Winners 1964
Beryl Hughes, Silver Medal (left); Anne Capper, Gold Medal (centre); Janet Frazer, John Hill Abram prize after their presentation from Lady Woolton

Presentations

Prize Winners April 1965

Mr W.L. Bateson, Janet Webber, Miss R. Haynes, Diane Gilbride, Countess of Derby, Matron S. Jackson, Elizabeth Parry, Moira O'Hara, Professor F. Stock

Prize Winners April 1966
Miss L. Robertson, Doctor Emyr Wyn Jones, Kathleen Williams, Judith McDonald, Gold Medal, Miss L. Poueits, Miss A. White, Miss R. Darroch, Sylvia Moorcroft and Elizabeth Buckley, joint Silver Medal, Mr W. L. Bateson, Miss R. Haynes

Miss Mary Jones, Matron T. Turner and Sister R. Darroch with Staff Nurses 1949

Newly Qualified Staff Nurses 1953

Groups

Group Photograph with The Countess of Sefton 1956

Matron S. Jackson with Sisters circa 1957

Groups

Group photograph 1961

Newly qualified Staff Nurses 1961

New Staff Nurses 1963

Group photograph 1963

Newly qualified Staff Nurses 1965 (January 1962 PTS)

Group photograph with The Countess of Derby April 1965

Group photograph 1966
Miss L. Poueits presented the prizes and certificates and Miss R. Darroch gave the address

REUNIONS

Portmeirion Lunch June 1999

Reunions

Reunion Lunch
Portmeirion Hotel, North Wales June 2002

Gwynedd Nurses
Portmeirion June 2006

Reunions

70th Anniversary of Nurses' League
Miss Jean Woods, President October 2003

Arriving for the Reunion
October 2005

Reunions

August 1955 PTS celebrate their 50th Anniversary
October 2005

Nurses' League Committee Members
After the A.G.M. October 2006

Reunions

Meeting friends in the Old Chapel after the A.G.M.
October 2007

Tea at the Reunion in the Foresight Centre
October 2007

MEMORABILIA

Hospital Badge

Awarded to all Staff Nurses who
completed their 4th year

Gold Medal

Awarded to the Nurse
of the Year

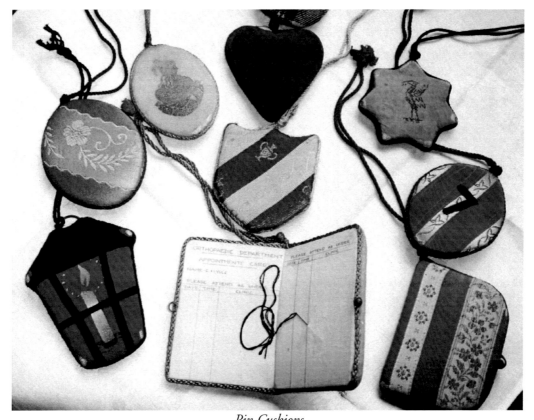

Pin Cushions
Examples of Pin Cushions made by Ward Sisters to present to their staff at Christmas. This tradition was discontinued circa 1961

Memorabilia

A Nightingale Lamp
An example of the lamps used in the Royal Infirmary, before electricity was introduced

THE FUTURE...

Restoration work by Liverpool University to Ward 12 1998

The Future...

Restoration to Ward 9

Refurbished Outpatient Department Upper Floor

GLOSSARY

Clarence Ward
Named after H.R.H. The Duke of Clarence and Avondale, a grandson of Queen Victoria, who opened the Royal Infirmary in 1890.

Red Rose Ball
A fundraising event held annually between 1929 and 1939, usually at the Adelphi Hotel, Liverpool to support the voluntary hospitals.

Walter Harding
A local businessman and benefactor who, in 1929, donated a tennis trophy to be competed for annually by Liverpool Hospitals. The library in the Nurses Home was named after him.

Medals and Prizes
- Gold Medal – the Marjorie Fisher Bradfield prize. Marjorie Fisher Bradfield trained at the Royal around 1920 and married a Minister who became the Bishop of Bath and Wells. When she died in 1953, the family endowed money to fund the Gold Medal. In 1954, the Bishop unveiled a Memorial Window in the Chapel in memory of past members of the nursing staff of the Royal.
- Prize for the best Medical Nurse was donated in memory of Professor John Hill Abram, Physician. An annual award of 10 guineas.
- Sir John Shute Memorial Prize was awarded annually. Sir John Shute was Chairman of the House Committee for many years.
- The Elizabeth Pearson prize was awarded in memory of a trainee nurse.

- The Mrs Stanley Morris prize was awarded to the Silver Medallist.

Marion Agnes Gullen Trophy
A national competition with an eliminating round in the form of an essay on nursing. The finals were held in London and involved demonstrating practical nursing skills. Marion Agnes Gullen was a Sister Tutor at St. Thomas's Hospital and one of the instigators of the common syllabus for nurse training which commenced in the 1920s.

Portmeirion Reunion
This is an informal reunion of past L.R.I. nurses who meet for lunch in June each year, at Portmeirion, North Wales.

The Liverpool Royal Infirmary Training School Nurses' League
The Nurses' League was inaugurated in 1933 by Miss Mary Jones, Matron of the Royal Infirmary. An annual reunion is held on the third Saturday in October, in the former Chapel of the Liverpool Royal Infirmary, now the Foresight Centre.

Website: www.rinursesleague.org.uk